When It Is Hot

By Liza Charlesworth

ISBN: 978-1-339-02774-6

Art Director: Tannaz Fassihi; Designer: Tanya Chernyak
Photos ©: p8: Matt Gerlach/Shutterstock.com. All other photos © Getty Images.
Copyright © Liza Charlesworth. All rights reserved. Published by Scholastic Inc.

1 2 3 4 5 6 7 8 9 10   68   32 31 30 29 28 27 26 25 24 23

Printed in Jiaxing, China. First printing, August 2023.

■SCHOLASTIC

It gets hot in the summer!
When it is hot,
you can swim a lot.

When it is hot,
you can hit a ball
with a bat. Whack!

You can skip
on the sand
with a pal.

You can run
and romp
in the sun.

You can go fast on a path.
Whiz, whiz, whiz!

You can sniff and whiff.
Which smell of summer
is the best? Mmmmm!

Pop!

When it is hot,
you can sit on the grass
and see big pops of light.

Wham, crack, bam!
Wham, crack, bam!
Whisssssssss!